The Red Mason Bee:

Taking the Sting Out of Bee-keeping

A practical guide to managing
Osmia rufa as a pollinator in gardens,
allotments, and orchards

by

Christopher O'Toole

(Head of the Bee Systematics and Biology Unit,
Hope Entomological Collections,
Oxford University Museum of Natural History)

Osmia **Publications, Banbury**

First published in 2000 by *Osmia* Publications, Banbury

© *Osmia* Publications 2000

ISBN 09539906 05

A CIP record for this title is available from the British Library.

Cover photograph: A female Red Mason Bee, *Osmia rufa*, drinks nectar from a borage flower (*Borago officinalis*). © P. O'Toole.

Text edited by Neil Curtis.
Production by Neil Curtis Publishing Services.

Designed by **Mark-making Design**, Chipping Norton.

Printed and bound in Thailand by Gift Export Co., Ltd.

About the Author

Chris O'Toole has been studying wild bees for more than thirty years. He heads the Bee Systematics and Biology Unit at the Oxford University Museum of Natural History and is the author of many books on insect natural history including (with Anthony Raw) *Bees of the World*.

He is also a frequent broadcaster on radio and has been involved in the production of many television programmes in natural history, most notably the BBC television series *Alien Empire*, for which he wrote the accompanying book of the same name.

His research interests include the nesting biology of the Red Mason Bee, *Osmia rufa*, and the systematics, biogeography, and floral relations of Mediterranean bees.

Chris O'Toole is the founder of the Oxford Bee Company Limited, a spinout company of Oxford University established in conjunction with Isis Innovation Ltd.

Acknowledgements: I thank my wife Rose for her constant support and encouragement and for holding the vision of the Oxford Bee Company Limited. I also thank Dr Peter Hotten of Isis Innovation Ltd, the technology transfer company of Oxford University, for facilitating the gestation and final delivery of our baby.

I am indebted to Larry Snell for making available his wisdom and skills in the business world, and for having the courage to invest his life in the OBC. I thank my mother-in-law, Lina Cuff, for tolerating with great good humour and generosity of spirit, the temporary invasion of her house by the OBC and its staff.

The excellent illustrations in this book are a tribute to the skills of four photographers, and I thank Rod and Ken Preston-Mafham of Premaphotos Wildlife and my brother, Peter O'Toole. I also thank my old friend and fellow bee enthusiast, Dr Anthony Raw, not only for two excellent photographs, but also for stimulating my interest in *Osmia rufa* all those years ago.

Finally, I thank all those friends and relatives who have allowed me to use their gardens as propagation plots for the Red Mason bee.

Contents

1 *Osmia rufa* as a pollination pet 1

2 The natural history of the Red Mason Bee, *Osmia rufa* 3

3 Using nester kits for the Red Mason Bee 11

    1 In gardens and allotments 12

    2 In orchards 13

    3 In greenhouses and polytunnels 14

    4 Overwintering: garden-, allotment-, and orchard-reared bees 15

4 Frequently asked questions 16

5 The need to conserve our wild bees and what you can do 20

6 Other solitary bees managed for pollination 22

7 Where to get your bee nester kits 24

    Further reading 25

    Field notes 26

The colour plates

1 A worker honeybee, *Apis mellifera*, at apple blossom

2 A worker garden bumblebee, *Bombus hortorum*

3 A female of the Dune Mason Bee, *Osmia aurulenta*, seals her completed nest

4 A mating pair of the Red Mason Bee, *Osmia rufa*

5 A female leafcutter bee, *Megachile willughbiella*, cuts a piece of rose leaf

6 Emerging from her 'quarry', a female *Osmia rufa* bears a glistening pellet of mud between her jaws

7 Carrying her ball of mud, a female *Osmia rufa* returns to her nest in an old garden cane

8 Four completed cells of *Osmia rufa*

9 Feeding larvae of *Osmia rufa*

10 A female *Osmia rufa* covered with hundreds of mites, *Chaetodactylus osmiae*

11 A nest cell of *Osmia rufa* (left) infested by larvae of the kleptoparasitic fly, *Cacoxenus indagator*

12 A pollen-dusted female of *Osmia rufa* returns to her nest

13 The nest kits supplied by the Oxford Bee Company Limited

ONE
Osmia rufa as a pollination pet

We are all familiar with the idea of putting out nest boxes for birds. It is a delight to watch, say, a pair of blue tits rearing their young through spring. And there is a real satisfaction to be had in knowing that one is providing a home for these lovely creatures, a feeling of being involved in the conservation of wildlife.

There are similar pleasures to be had in providing nests for hedgehogs and dormice or roosts for bats. Now it is possible to do the same for the Red Mason Bee, *Osmia rufa*. And, as well as helping in the conservation of these important insects, there is an opportunity to play an active role in managing the pollination ecology of your garden, allotment, or orchard.

With the nester kits described below, you can become a bee rancher and see increased yields in your fruit and vegetable crops. *Osmia rufa* will readily use the nests and you can enjoy watching your bees returning with pollen to the homes you have provided. And you don't have to get dressed up in protective suits and veils: *Osmia rufa* takes the sting out of bee-keeping; it is a docile but hard-working bee and is thus an ideal pollination pet for the garden.

Sex and flowering plants

Like us, flowering plants are sexual organisms. And pollination is the process by which male cells, pollen, are transferred from the male organs, the anthers, to the stigma, the receptive, female part of the flower. Most flowering plants are self-incompatible, that is, each must receive pollen from another individual plant of the same species if fertilization and seed set are to occur.

Being rooted, literally, to the spot, plants need some agent to help them transport pollen from one individual to another. Some, such as pines, oaks, willows, and grasses, are adapted for pollination by wind: they produce billions of very tiny, light pollen grains from very exposed flowers. But the majority of flowering plants are pollinated by insects and have evolved various ways and means of recruiting them for the business of mating by proxy. The visual impact of a flower-rich garden is largely a reflection of this: the herbaceous border is a sea of rampant sexuality, with brightly coloured petals and sweet scents designed to attract insects, especially bees.

We can liken the relationship between flowering plants and bees to a market place, where retailers (the plants) use colour and scent to advertise their wares (pollen and nectar) to a band of discriminating consumers (bees). This economy is based on two currencies, energy and time. And both partners have to spend some of this currency to buy themselves into the market. The plants expend time and energy in advertising and manufacturing pollen and nectar. And the female bees have already invested time and energy in mating, and in seeking and building a nest, before they venture into the market place.

Nectar is an energy-rich mixture of sugars which fuels the bees' activities and which some, such as the honeybee and bumblebees, convert into honey which they store as a source of energy. And pollen is rich in protein and minerals. Plants produce more pollen than is needed for reproduction, this excess being an offered reward for the bee's pollinating services.

Vegetarian wasps

Bees are hunting wasps that became vegetarians. Instead of preying on other insects, bees gather pollen and nectar as food for their larvae. And, in scrabbling about for pollen, a female bee becomes dusted with millions of pollen grains; when she next visits a plant of the same species, some of these pollen grains are inevitably brushed off on to the receptive female part of the flower, the stigma: pollination and, eventually, fertilization are accomplished.

Bees have evolved a number of adaptations to exploit the resources on offer from plants. They are densely clothed with branched, feathery hairs that easily trap pollen. And they have structures for the transport of consolidated masses of pollen. Some, such as the honeybees and bumblebees, each has a pollen basket on the outer face of the hind leg. This takes the form of an expanded and slightly concave surface fringed with stiff bristles. The bees use their legs to remove pollen from the body hairs and pass it back to the hind legs. Here, mixed with a little nectar to make it sticky, they build it up to form a solid mass (Plate 1).

Other bees, such as the mining bees which nest in the ground, have a dense brush of specialized hairs on the hind legs called the scopa. Here they consolidate a rather dry mass of pollen. And the leaf-cutter bees and mason bees, including our *Osmia rufa*, have their scopa in the form of dense fringes of stiff hairs on the underside of the abdomen (Plate 7).

Bees have evolved longer tongues so that they can probe deep-tube flowers for nectar (Plate 2).

The bee–flower relationship is a co-evolved partnership that took millions of years to refine, and much of the life on this planet is directly dependent on it. You can benefit directly from this partnership by keeping the Red Mason Bee in your own garden, allotment, or orchard. They are fun and easy to keep, safe with children and pets, and you will be helping in the conservation of ecologically important insects.

TWO
The natural history
of the Red Mason Bee, *Osmia rufa*

Life history

Osmia rufa is a solitary bee. That is, each nest is the work of a single female, working alone; there is no caste of workers such as are found in the social honeybee and bumblebees. In fact, these familiar bees are in a distinct minority: the vast majority of bees are solitary just like *O. rufa*. And, unlike the social bees, there is no overlap of generations: a female solitary bee never lives to see her offspring.

Most solitary bees are mining bees that excavate nest tunnels and brood cells in the ground. The females of these bees line their cells with a glandular secretion which is waterproof and resistant to bacteria and fungi.

By contrast, *O. rufa* belongs to a group of cavity-nesters, the mason and leaf-cutter bees. These bees have three things in common:

1 the females nest in pre-existing cavities such as hollow plant stems or beetle borings in dead wood;
2 instead of using a glandular secretion, they collect, according to species, substances such as mud, leaf pieces, resin, and tiny pebbles;
3 the tract of specialized pollen-transporting hairs, the scopa, is situated on the underside of the abdomen.

O. rufa uses mud as a building material. Other species of mason bee, such as *Osmia aurulenta*, use a mastic of finely chewed leaves. This little bee specializes exclusively in using empty snail shells as nests (*see* Plate 3).

O. rufa is widespread and common in England and Wales and extends northwards into Scotland as far as Edinburgh. It is widely distributed in continental Europe and even penetrates into the Mediterranean region.

In Britain, the natural nest sites of *O. rufa* would normally be found in old, mature hedgerows and along ragged woodland edges where one might expect to find plenty of old bramble and hogweed stems with broken ends or dead wood and fallen trees. With the loss of much of our hedgerows (*see* Section 5), however, many of these nest sites have disappeared. And this is why domestic gardens assume such importance, not just for *O. rufa* but for a wide range of solitary bees.

For example, several species of leaf-cutter bee (*Megachile* spp.: Plate 5) are now, like *Osmia rufa*, largely associated with domestic gardens: the contrived floral diversity of the typical garden, together with its structural complexity, provide abundant forage and nest sites.

Over the years, I have found *O. rufa* nesting in a wide range of places associated with people and their gardens. These include: old, discarded lengths of garden cane; old locks in greenhouses; holes in large pieces of flint being used as garden ornaments; nail holes in old fence posts and mortar; air bricks; and spaces among thatch and roofing tiles. *O. rufa* is a spring bee, and the earliest individuals are tempted out by the first really mild days in mid- to late March. It is the males that put in this early appearance. The females emerge between a week and ten days later and are active until the end of June to mid-July.

Like the females, the males are covered with a dense, gingery fur but they are more slender and have a dense tuft of white hairs on the front of the head (Plate 4). Males are 6-11 millimetres (mm) long while the more robust females are 10-16 mm in length. The female's head is entirely black haired and is larger and squarer than that of the males. This is to accommodate the large muscles associated with the powerful jaws used to excavate mud.

After emergence, the males spend their time feeding on nectar at flowers and flying in an agitated manner around nest entrances, waiting for the females to appear. Males are aggressive towards each other and often jostle for position on some vantage point close to nests. Like those of all bees, the males of *O. rufa* do not have a sting.

When the females begin to emerge, there is a mad scramble between the males to be the first to mate. The reason for the extreme competitiveness between males is that the females usually mate only once so that the males are very quickly confronted with a rapidly diminishing resource in the form of virgin, nubile females. A female needs to mate only once because she stores sperm in a special sac, the spermatheca, with a single mating providing more than enough sperm to fertilize her complement of about forty eggs.

With such a stressful and competitive life-style, the males quickly become ragged and worn, with patches of abraded fur and increasingly frayed wings. Eventually, after about three to four weeks, they die, leaving the females to continue their work of nesting and foraging.

Immediately after emergence, a female *Osmia rufa* seeks a patch of suitable flowers on which to feed. She needs sugar-rich nectar to fuel all her activities, as well as pollen as a source of protein to complete the maturation of the eggs in her ovaries. Because *O. rufa* is a spring bee and warm weather is not a guaranteed constant, a female may frequently become chilled, and you can often see them sunning themselves on a leaf or flower or roosting on a warm stone to absorb heat.

During this early period of feeding, she will have to run the gauntlet of mate-hungry males which probably detect her presence by scent as well as by visual clues; as well as nest sites, males often patrol feeding areas that are attractive to females. Our female will be pounced on time and again, sometimes by several males at once, all of which she rejects with a sudden loud buzzing noise made by rapidly vibrating her wing tips. Eventually, however, she will select a male and the mating process begins.

Mating lasts between five and ten minutes, with the male mounting the female from on top (Plate 4). Periodically, the female emits a sudden sharp buzz while the male sits with his much longer antennae held forward and downwards in a characteristic pose. Mating may take place on a leaf or on the ground and, during the process, the female may occasionally walk around, carrying the male. Throughout, the mating pair is highly attractive to other males which often pounce on them and try to dislodge the mating male. I have seen this happen many times but have never seen any male successfully usurp a mating rival.

After mating, both sexes spend a lot of time grooming themselves, using legs to smooth down pubescence and clean wings. Eventually, the male takes to the wing and is engaged once more in the pursuit of mates. But, for our female, the serious business of nesting now begins.

When she finds a potential nest site, she inspects it carefully by tapping her antennae rapidly around the entrance before entering for a more detailed examination. You can follow what a female is doing inside her nest by using a mirror to shine a beam of light into the nest. And this is what you might see: if the prospective nest is an old beetle boring in wood, then she will probably have to clear out remains of old wood fibres and beetle droppings. She will repeatedly back out to the nest entrance, using her abdomen to push debris to the outside. If the nest was, in fact, used as a nest by a female of the previous season's generation of *O. rufa*, then you can see her clearing out the remains of left-over pollen, cocoons, and the mud partitions between cells.

If our female decides on this particular cavity as her first nest, she may spend some time roosting in it, sitting just inside the entrance. Indeed, by this time, it might be dusk and she will spend the night in her newly chosen home.

As soon as the first sun warms the entrance next morning, our female will begin to stir. She will need to refuel on nectar at the nearest suitable flowers but, before she can do this, she must do something that all foragers from a fixed home base must do: learn her surroundings and memorize cues that will enable her to find her way back to her newly acquired desirable residence.

Like the females of all wasps and bees, *O. rufa* has a whole repertoire of behaviours at her disposal that enable her to do just that and in a very precise way.

The first piece of behaviour may well be what initially attracts your attention to females nesting in your garden – that is, a female flying repeatedly in a side-to-side, figure-of-eight pattern about what seems to be a central point, namely, her nest entrance. Such a female is memorizing visual landmarks close to her nest, such as a stone to one side, a clump of flowers next to this, an old plant pot on the other side, and a patch of lichen above the nest.

If you watch for long enough, you will see the female widen the sweep of her repetitive figures-of-eight and, at the same time, fly slightly higher and further away. She is now beginning to memorize landmarks that are further away from her nest entrance. She will increase the distance and breadth of her sweeps until she is starting to memorize more distant cues on her horizon. These could include a prominent tree, a church steeple, and a faraway hill.

Our female will repeat these actions until she has a detailed mental map of her immediate and distant surroundings. She is now ready for that all-too-urgent refuelling trip and she will set off for a good feed. In so doing, the memorizing continues: she remembers other landmarks and the direction of the nest from which she has flown. This last feat is truly remarkable and just how she does it is a tribute to the efficiency of her tiny brain.

In addition to her ability to construct a mental map of her surroundings, the female bee is also able to memorize the position of the sun relative to her nest entrance as she flies away from it. Now you might think that the sun is not an ideal reference point. After all, it does have the irritating habit of moving across the sky as the day progresses. But our *Osmia* is not in the least fazed by this: she has an on-board clock which enables her to compensate for the sun's movements. But what if clouds obscure the sun? Well, she has another skill at her disposal: her eyes are able to detect the plane of polarized light, so that she knows where the sun is, even if you and I don't and even if there is total cloud cover.

Now our female can feed in earnest and find her way home. Back at the nest, she will make a number of orientation flights just to fine-tune her memorized landmarks. And now, the business of nesting can begin properly.

By now, our female will have a pretty good idea of where the local food supplies are to be found: she will know where the best nectar and pollen sources are, having spent some time foraging to meet her own immediate needs. But there is one more resource she needs to reconnoitre: mud. She needs a source of, preferably, fine-grained soil that she can convert into mud of just the right texture for her building requirements. Her first post-feeding foraging trip will be for mud rather than for pollen. And this is because her first task is to plaster the rear end of her nest tunnel with a smooth layer of mud.

You may detect females in their search for mud because they fly in a very characteristic pattern: low passes over bare earth, with frequent landings to test the texture of the soil. Sometimes you may see several to many females doing this in the same place because they will all be attracted to the same sort of soil.

Eventually, our female will find just the right spot and start loosening soil with her powerful jaws, adding saliva, if necessary, to render it into a malleable paste. Soon the female will have a ball of glistening mud nearly as big as her head (Plate 6). Now she carries this back to her nest (Plate 7) and applies it to the rear of the tunnel. She may make two or three mud-gathering trips before she has finished. And, having found a suitable area of soil, she will return again and again throughout her nesting cycle, to what becomes a quarry in miniature. Indeed, several females may use the same quarry and may be seen disappearing into the hole they have excavated, behaviour that has led to erroneous reports that *O. rufa* sometimes nests in the ground.

I discovered one day just how important a good source of suitably textured soil is. In 1997, we moved to our present house in Banbury, part of a Victorian terrace with long, narrow back gardens. In the spring of 1998, I ordered 2 tonnes of topsoil to be delivered. It arrived at 7.30 one Saturday morning and, by half-past nine, there was quite a swarm of *O. rufa* females excavating mud and flying off. At that time I had no occupied nests in this garden, my nesting population being housed in a Loughborough garden, so these bees were not 'mine'.

There were enough bees to form a visible flight line, coming and going from the soil heap, flying down the garden towards the house, then veering upwards and to the left, along the roof ridges of the adjacent houses, and then diagonally over the roof of a church. I went out into the street and picked up the line of bees as they flew diagonally across the street and then over the roofs of the houses about 50 metres away on the opposite side. At this point I lost them but this observation demonstrates just how efficient the females of *O. rufa* are in finding a newly created resource, in this case, a two-hour-old heap of soil at least 250 metres from their nearest possible nest sites.

After smoothing the inner application of mud, the female begins her next task: foraging for pollen. She will visit a wide range of flowers and she quickly learns which are the most abundant sources of pollen and nectar at any particular time. When fruit trees such as plum, apple, pear, and cherry are in full flower, she will major on these for pollen, sometimes visiting other plants for nectar.

When she visits, say, an apple tree, she will land on a flower and scrabble for pollen, using her legs to loosen it from the anthers. Soon she becomes dusted with the yellow powder and begins to compact it in the dense brush of hairs forming the scopa on the underside of her abdomen. She is not as efficient as the honeybee in grooming herself, however, and plenty of pollen remains on all areas of her body. It is this that makes her such an ideal pollinator: her less-than-perfect grooming means that pollen is easily dislodged on to the receptive stigma when she visits the flowers of another tree.

It takes between eight and fifteen foraging trips to gather enough pollen to provision a cell. You can tell how many pollen loads a cell has because, if you open up a completed one before the egg has hatched and the larva has started feeding, you can see the different layers of pollen, each one representing a single foraging trip. If your female has visited different plants on successive trips, you can often see pollen layers of different colours. Every now and then, the female adds a little nectar to the pollen mass.

The reason for the variation in the numbers of foraging trips is to do with the sex of her offspring: female bees are larger and their larvae need more food while the more slender males need less pollen. Sometimes, a female makes a mistake and lays a male egg in a female cell and a giant male is the result the following spring; and the opposite happens if, by mistake, a female lays a female egg in a male cell – a dwarf daughter is the result.

The deeper cells in the nest almost always contain females while the outermost cells are almost always male.

When our female has fully provisioned her first cell, she lays a single, pearly white egg on top of the pollen (Plate 8). She then gathers enough mud to build a wall of mud which seals the cell. She repeats the process until she has provisioned a row of cells, each with a single egg and partitioned from its neighbour by a mud wall. The final cell to be completed is always about 1-2 centimetres (cm) from the nest entrance. She then seals the nest with mud, leaving an empty, vestibular cell between the nest closure and the first cell. This is believed to be a deterrent to certain parasites which lay their eggs in *Osmia* nests (*see* below).

The number of cells per nest depends on the length of the cavity used. The tubes comprising the nest kits supplied by the Oxford Bee Company Limited. usually have six to eight cells.

After completing her first nest, the female will start another one in a nearby tube. In her short adult life of ten to twelve weeks, she might make a total of four to five nests.

The female's life's work involves a complex sequence of stereotyped behaviours:

nest searching → nest inspection → mud gathering → mud application → pollen gathering → egg laying → mud gathering → mud application → pollen gathering, and so on.

Here, the completion of one task is the stimulus to begin the next task in the sequence.

I never cease to be impressed by the skills of these and other nesting wasps and bees. Consider the processing power that makes the nesting cycle possible, as well as the homing abilities described above, and all this is accomplished with an on-board computer about the size of a grain of salt!

All the while she has been nesting, our female has not been alone: though a solitary species, *O. rufa* likes to nest gregariously, and several females may use a nest kit simultaneously.

As a typical solitary bee, a female *O. rufa* does not live to see her offspring. Towards the end of June, the females are becoming worn and tattered: the bright foxy red of a female's fur will by now have been bleached grey by the sun, and the middle of her thorax and abdomen may well be bald because of constant abrasion against the nest walls. The ends of her wings will be badly frayed, too.

Very old females can often be seen sitting at the nest entrances, usually showing a distinct tremor, and it is now that some very old females may show distinct signs of senile behaviour: a female may provision and seal cells without laying an egg, or, more often, simply partition completely empty cells. Perhaps this behaviour indicates that she has run out of eggs.

Eventually, the females die but already their offspring are active: the eggs will have hatched into tiny larvae which begin to feed voraciously on the stored pollen for most of the summer. Initially, the larva's soft cuticle can expand as it increases in size (Plate 9) but, eventually, the larva must moult its skin. During the feeding and developmental period, each larva moults four or five times. When the larva is fully grown, there is little or no pollen left. Eventually, at about mid-August to the beginning of September, the larva spins a tough brown cocoon (Plate 11) and enters the pupal stage. During this period, larval tissues are broken down and reassembled to form the adult bee.

The bees become adult in late September to early October, and remain inside their cocoons until the following spring, when they emerge and begin the cycle anew.

Nest associates

Nesting birds have a number of hangers-on – species such as dermestid beetles (sometimes called carpet beetles) – that feed on feather and skin debris which accumulates at the bottom of the nest.

Nesting bees also have their associates and *Osmia rufa* is no exception; their nests are host to several species of mite, principally *Chaetodactylus osmiae*. Mites are tiny relatives of spiders and, as its name implies, this one is a specialist in the nests of *Osmia* species.

The mites enter the nest cells when the female bee is away on a foraging trip. They feed on uneaten pollen left by larvae. In this capacity they are best described as associates acting as scavengers. But, when present in large numbers, they eat the bee egg and consume the pollen, and breed and multiply within the pollen mass. In the following spring, any adult bee which emerges from behind a mite-infested cell bites its way through the cell on its way to make its first emergence and, in so doing, picks up hundreds or even thousands of the tiny mites which cover her entire body.

When the bee first visits a flower many of the mites jump off and remain to infest another *Osmia* when it visits and they are then transported back to her nest (Plate 10).

I have noticed that, if a male bee is infested with mites, they eventually congregate at the end of its abdomen, close to the genitalia. Indeed, when, in the course of research I had to dissect the genitalia of males, I often found that the genital cavity was packed with mites. I surmised that this was to facilitate the venereal transmission of the mites and, sure enough, when I once found a mating pair in which the male was heavily infested, I was able to see, with the aid of a magnifying glass, the mites leaving the male to climb on to the female's body. She was then primed to infect her nest when she began one.

Enemies

Like all animals and plants, *Osmia rufa* has natural enemies. Some are generalist predators, such as birds and spiders, but others are much more specialized and are adapted to prey specifically on *O. rufa* and its close bee relatives.

Those sometimes found attacking *Osmia rufa* include a fly, a beetle, and two species of wasp; none of them has a common name.

The fly is *Cacoxenus indagator*, and its females loiter with egg-laying intent around *Osmia rufa* nest entrances. When a female bee has departed on a foraging trip, the female fly enters the nest and lays a clutch of eggs. After the female bee has finished and sealed that particular cell, the fly eggs hatch much earlier than the bee egg and the larvae feed voraciously on the stored pollen. The result is that, when the bee egg hatches, there is insufficient food to support development and the bee larva starves to death. Technically, therefore, the larva of *Cacoxenus* is a kleptoparasite, a parasite that kills its host, not by attacking it directly, but by stealing its food.

The single pollen mass is enough to support the development of fifteen to twenty fly larvae. Cells which have been infested with this are easy to identify: they are filled with a dense yellow mass of the long, coiled, ribbon-like faecal threads of the fly larvae (Plate 11).

The beetle enemy is called *Ptinus sexmaculatus* and, like the fly, its larvae live as kleptoparasites (see above) in the nests of *Osmia rufa*, eating the stored pollen.

The wasp enemies of *Osmia rufa* do attack their host directly. One of them is a tiny, metallic-green insect about 2 mm long and is called *Monodontomerus obscurus*. Members of this species attack only long after the cell is completed, sealed, and the bee larva is well grown. The female wasp has an egg-laying tube, or ovipositor, protruding from the end of her abdomen, and she uses this to inject eggs through the side of a plant stem into an *Osmia* cell. Here the eggs hatch out and the larvae feed as parasites on the bee larva, eventually killing it. A single larva of *Osmia rufa* will support the development of fifteen to twenty of these tiny wasps.

The design of the Oxford Bee Company Limited. nest tubes protects your bees from this enemy: the combination of tough cardboard guard tube and inner liner makes it impossible for the *Monodontomerus* female to penetrate the cell with her ovipositor.

The other wasp parasite is much larger, about 10-12 mm long. It is called *Sapyga clavicornis*, and a female enters a cell while the bee is away foraging. She lays one or two eggs and these hatch before that of the bee. The first thing these larvae do is eat the bee egg before they go on to complete their development by feeding on the stored pollen. In Britain, this parasite is not very commonly found attacking *Osmia rufa*.

THREE
Using nester kits for the Red Mason Bee

Background to the nest design

A nester kit comprises an outer plastic cylinder containing cardboard nest tubes, each of which contains a removable paper liner (Plate 12). The liner is held in place at the rear of the tube by a plastic stopper that also functions as a grip when removing the liner. The lined tubes are a modification of a design devised for the North American Blue Orchard Mason Bee, *Osmia lignaria*, by Dr Phil Torchio. We have changed the dimensions of the nest tubes slightly to those which are best for *O. rufa*.

The advantage of the liner is that it can be removed at the end of the season and held up against a bright light so that the nest may be checked for cells that contain bees killed by disease or parasites. The dead cells can be removed and whole, healthy cocoons transferred to a fresh tube.

The combination of the thick outer cardboard tube and inner liner provides protection against one of the worst enemies of *Osmia rufa*, a tiny chalcidoid wasp, *Monodontomerus obscurus* (see Section 2 above on enemies).

The nest kits mimic the natural nest sites of *Osmia rufa* – hollow plant stems and beetle borings in dead wood. There are three reasons why they are so effective as nests, and they all centre on time, that all-important resource for a bee that is active for a relatively short period in a season where the weather can be unpredictable:

1 each kit provides a concentrated array of nests in a single place, so nest-seeking females at the beginning of the season are saved much time because, once they have found a nest kit and completed their first nests, they do not have to search again for another suitable nest cavity;

2 with new nest kits, a female does not have to spend time cleaning out the usual debris – beetle droppings, wood fibres, pith, etc. – which is to be found in natural nest sites (although, if she is using a tube in a nest kit used the previous season, she will have to invest time in some cleaning work but the smooth nest interior makes this a much easier task);

3 with the new nest kits, the constant internal dimensions require minimal amounts of mud for cell partitions and nest closure. By contrast, irregularly shaped cavities, such as the normal nest sites and places such as cavities in stones and old walls, require much more mud to reduce spaces down to normal cell size and, consequently, a larger investment in time and energy in gathering extra mud.

Propagation

1 In gardens and allotments

Most urban and suburban areas in England, Wales, and southern Scotland have wild populations of the Red Mason Bee, *Osmia rufa*. Because their nest sites tend to be scattered, the bees are easily overlooked and you may have a healthy population in your neighbourhood without realizing it.

The best places to site your nests are sheltered, sunny spots, facing south-east or south-west. A site that gets early morning sun is perfect and, if you have a sheltered, east-facing spot, this is ideal. Avoid north-facing situations at all costs.

Ensure that overhanging or trailing vegetation does not obscure your nests. You may think that you are helping the bees (and your fruit set!) by placing the nests as closely as possible to fruit trees, but the bees do not like dappled shade or nests which are moved by wind, so do not attach nests directly to trees. The bees are quite capable of finding your fruit blossoms and any other flowers you want them to visit.

It is also important to make sure that the nests are well above ground to avoid them being splashed with soil during heavy rain.

So, where are the best places to put your nests? More than thirty years of experience have taught me that placing nests on isolated wooden or metal stakes in the middle of a garden is not very successful to gain high rates of occupation. My greatest success has been with nests placed on walls which are at least 75 cm (29-30 in) high or attached to wooden fence posts. Other suitable nest sites include the eaves of garden sheds and garages, especially if they are made of wood or among log piles. Log piles are particularly good because females are attracted to them in search of beetle borings and emergence holes.

On allotments, the eaves of wooden sheds are good sites for nests. Walls and wooden fences are not always features of allotments and, if they are lacking in yours, then the best place to position your nests is in a raised, south- or south-east-facing location at the edge of your plot. Old wooden boxes are ideal. If you grow onions for seed, you will find that *O. rufa* is an excellent pollinator.

All of these situations are in marginal positions, at the edges of things, and I think the reason for their success is that the richest sources of natural nest sites are hedgerows and woodland edges, both of which are marginal. In other words, the bees are programmed to search along edges.

As well as providing nest sites for your bees, you can help them by planting plants and shrubs of which they are particularly fond. If you have a good mix of fruit trees, raspberries, and early flowering strawberries, then you are in business. If there are horse chestnut trees in your vicinity, you are doubly lucky: *Osmia rufa* loves the blossom and will fly several hundred metres from the nest to feed at these bounteous blossoms.

Additionally, the mix of species described in Section 5 is excellent but I would single out the beautiful blue flowers of borage *(Borago officinalis)*, geraniums, and wallflowers, as well as the shrub *Pieris japonica*.

When your nests have attracted bees, their nesting activities will be very obvious and you can have hours of fun watching them. A mud seal indicates a completed nest. In a good season you may achieve almost 100 per cent occupancy of your nest tubes. If you wish to expand in the following season, you can always obtain additional nest kits from the Oxford Bee Company Limited.

If you decide to have more than one nest kit, then it is a good idea to locate them in twos in different locations about the garden, rather than concentrate them all in the same place. But do remember the general rules about aspect and positioning. In some areas, earwigs my break open sealed,completed nests. If this is a problem,smear some petroleum jelly (Vaseline) around the point of attachment of your nest kit.

2 In orchards

For the positioning of nesters in orchards, the same considerations apply as in gardens: do not place nests in fruit trees. Instead, place them in raised situations at the edge of your plot. As with allotments, wooden shelters raised well off the ground are ideal. It is a good idea to stretch chicken wire over the entrance to the shelter: this does not impede the bees but does protect against woodpeckers which sometimes peck at nest tubes and damage them.

There may be no patches of bare earth in your orchard so it is a good idea to create some around your plot to provide the bees with a ready source of building materials. Alternatively, you can distribute around the orchard seed trays containing crumbly, aerated soil. If this gets too dry, add just a little water – a momentary spray from a watering can will be sufficient.

The nesters should be evenly distributed around your orchard's margins. As a rule of thumb, 500 *Osmia rufa* females will adequately pollinate 1 hectare (2.5 acres) of apples at commercial densities. The design of nest supplied by the Oxford Bee Company Limited. ensures a sex ratio of roughly fifty-fifty males to females and, with an average of eight cells per nest tube, you can expect four females to develop in each occupied tube. Thus, once you have built up your nesting populations, 125 occupied nests should produce enough bees to pollinate 1 hectare of apples.

This compares favourably with the honeybee for which the literature recommends an average of three honeybee colonies per hectare of apples, each with a minimum number of 20,000 active workers. Thus, 500 females of *Osmia rufa* will do the pollinating work of 60,000 honeybees, that is, one *O. rufa* female is the equivalent of 120 honeybee workers.

In practice, it is difficult to have built up honeybee populations to such sizes so early in the year, and more hives may have to be introduced to compensate. With apple and other rosaceous fruit crops, honeybees have a tendency to land directly on the petals so minimizing their direct contact with the pollen-bearing anthers, and they will often probe the flowers from the side to gain access to the nectaries without coming into contact with pollen. This is particularly prevalent with the 'Golden Delicious' variety of apples, one of the most commercially important crops.

By contrast, females of *Osmia rufa* come into direct contact with the sexual parts of the flower and are principally interested in handling pollen. All in all, then, *Osmia rufa* is a more efficient pollinator of orchard crops than the honeybee, and there is great potential for its commercial development. Nor do you have to get dressed up in a veil and protective clothing to manage them!

3 In greenhouses and polytunnels

If occupied nests of *Osmia rufa* are placed in greenhouses or polytunnels, the bees will readily take to the environment and complete their nesting cycle as normal.

They are particularly effective pollinators of strawberries, raspberries, and onions grown for seed.

It is important to protect the nests from extremes of temperature, and this is best achieved by placing them in raised wooden shelters with shelves positioned in such a way that there are air spaces above and below each shelf. The shelters should be deep enough to provide overhanging eaves to protect from direct sunlight.

The bees will need a source of mud for nest-building purposes, and you can meet those needs by putting some seed trays of crumbly, well-aerated soil around your greenhouse or polytunnel. Old potting compost is not suitable for this purpose.

4 Overwintering: garden-, allotment-, and orchard-reared bees

Leave your occupied nests in position until late September or early October. Until then, your bees are a little vulnerable and, if moved too soon, there may be some mortalities. Then remove the paper liners from occupied nests and place them in a cardboard box containing loosely crumpled newspaper for insulation. Before doing that, you can if you wish eliminate diseased or parasitized cells and put healthy cocoons in a fresh liner. Ensure the head end of the cocoon faces that which you decide to be the front of the nest. The head end has a cap or nipple in which the silk is less dense than the rest of the cocoon; the rear of the cocoon is uniform in colour and texture. You then have two choices. You can either:

place the box for the winter in an unheated shed or garage. The latter should not be attached to the house because then it will be too warm. In early spring, place the liners back into the outer guard tubes. If you are re-using guard tubes from the previous season, it is a good idea to use the rear, unweathered end of the guard tube as the front. Then use your judgement about when to place the nests back in their spot in the garden, allotment, or orchard. The beginning of March is usually a good time but take into consideration local weather conditions: is it a mild spring, or is the season a bit late? In northern areas it might be a good idea to delay placing the nests by about ten days;

or:

place your insulated box in the refrigerator and keep it there through the winter at 3-4 °C (38 °F). The bees will cope with this quite well, and the low temperatures may kill any parasites you might have missed. By refrigerating the bees, you can delay their emergence if the spring is late. In such circumstances, keep an eye on the weather and check with the long-range weather forecasts. About seven to ten days before you think the fine weather will begin, put your bees out on your plot.

FOUR
Frequently asked questions

Q1 *How can I be sure that Red Mason Bees will find and use my nests?*

A1 The females of *Osmia rufa* are very adept at finding suitable nest sites. If you have followed the instructions which came with the nest kit, the bees will find them. When you think of their natural nest sites – hollow plant stems and beetle borings in dead wood – these are not evenly distributed in the environment, especially in the garden situation. Thus, nest-seeking females in spring have simply got to be good at finding a scarce resource. By putting out nester kits, you are making life much easier for the bees. A condominium of this sort is bee heaven (Plates 12 and 13)! You have saved them time and effort. And this effort includes the labour that would have been involved in clearing out beetle and earwig droppings from borings and plant stems.

Once a female has started to use your nest kit, others will soon follow: they seem to be attracted to the activities of other females.

Q2 *Will the offspring of my bees use my nests the following season?*

A2 Yes. Females have a strong tendency to nest close to where they emerged. And they will re-use old nest tubes after clearing out the remains of the previous season's nest activity: old cell partitions, remains of pollen stores and cocoons. Moreover, the activities of the new generation of bees are attractive to other nest-seeking females in the area. After two or three years, however, the ends of the nest tubes closest to the entrances may become weathered and need replacing. You can order replacements and additional nest kits from the Oxford Bee Company Limited.

You can improve the chances of your bees' survival by overwintering them as described in the nest kit instructions or on page 15 of this book.

Q3 *The bee developing at the back of the nest is from the first egg to be laid and is therefore the oldest, so doesn't it wake up first in spring and don't the younger bees in front trap it?*

A3 This is the most frequently asked question and the answer is: yes and no! I discovered the answer when helping to make a television programme about solitary bees. We took a block of wood in which bees had nested in specially drilled tunnels in the previous season and sectioned one of the nests. The exposed section was covered with a piece of clear Perspex so that emergence of the bees in spring could be filmed. And, sure enough, we saw the answer to the question acted out in front of us. True to prediction, the oldest bee, that is, the one in the first and therefore deepest cell, woke up from winter hibernation first. Using her powerful jaws, she bit her way through the tough silk cocoon she had spun as a full-grown larva and then chewed through the mud partition separating her cell from that of the bee in front. She then bit into the cocoon of the bee in front of her and nipped its backside. This woke the bee and she, in turn, chewed through her cocoon and through the mud partition into the cell in front of her. And she, too, nipped the backside of the bee in front of her. In this way, a chain reaction was established and, in the course of half a day, all the bees in the nest tunnel had woken and were ready to start the cycle anew: mating, nesting, pollen- and mud-gathering, and egg-laying.

Q4 Are mason bees the same as 'masonry' bees, and can they damage my walls?

A4 No! Mason bees are called 'mason' bees for the same reason that some solitary wasps are called 'mason' wasps: they collect mud as a building material and they then mould it to form nest structures. *Osmia rufa* does often nest in pre-existing holes in soft mortar but does not actually excavate these cavities. This species is programmed to use pre-existing cavities such as hollow plant stems and beetle borings in dead wood. The sorts of holes in walls that *O. rufa* uses are irregular holes in soft, eroding mortar or old nail holes in mortar where nails were once used to support trellises, etc. Occasionally, *O. rufa* nests in airbricks and their mud nest closures block the vents.

It is unfortunate that *O. rufa* sometimes gets the blame for the activities of what can be called the 'true' masonry bee, *Colletes daviesanus*. This is a solitary mining bee with its normal nest site in sandy banks and cliffs. Unfortunately, the soft mortar in old walls mimics this bee's natural nesting sites so that they are often attracted in large numbers and may even pose a threat to the safety of the wall. It is not only old walls that are at risk: modern buildings thrown up by cowboy builders who have used too high a proportion of sand in their mortar mix are also threatened.

Q5 What can I do if I have Red Mason Bees nesting in my walls or in airbricks or between roof tiles?

A5 Don't panic! You can stage a rescue operation using nester kits from the Oxford Bee Company Limited. In late March to early April, just before the bees should start nesting, place a nester kit (or kits) close to where the bees are nesting inappropriately. When the females emerge and start looking for nest sites, they will often prefer the nice clean nests you have so kindly provided. The reason for this is simple: were they to re use the irregular cavities in the wall or spaces between roof tiles, the females would have to spend a lot of time and energy clearing out the debris from the previous year's nesting activities; by moving into your nice new apartment block, they are saved this labour. And, in the unpredictable climate of northern Europe, if time is not exactly money for these bees, it certainly has a value which can be translated into that most vital of resources: pollen!

Q6 Why are Red Mason Bees safe with children and pets?

A6 It is true that, like almost all female bees, the females of *Osmia rufa* each has a sting. They are not in the least bit aggressive, however, for the simple reason that they are solitary bees and, unlike the highly social honeybee, do not store large amounts of honey. Thus they do not have a large and valuable resource to protect.

I have worked with *O. rufa* for thirty years and I have handled females many times without being stung. For example, my work has involved pushing females to one side while using a mirror to direct a beam of light into a nest to observe a female's activities while she is within. In these circumstances, females have never responded aggressively. When, however, I knew that I would be encouraging people to keep these bees in their gardens, I thought I ought to find out just how much provocation was needed to induce a female to sting. I therefore took a female and rolled her between my fingers. Eventually she stung me and this was a mere pinprick, with none of the long-term pain and swelling one associates with stings from honeybees, bumblebees, and social wasps. Indeed, the sensory experience was all over in a couple of minutes.

The lesson here is simple and obvious: unless you handle a female *Osmia rufa* very roughly with your fingers, you are simply not going to get stung. This means it is quite safe for you and your children to observe these fascinating bees as closely as you please. And there is nothing at all to fear from the smaller males: like the males of all bees and wasps, they simply have no sting.

Q7 Which other solitary bees can I expect to use my nests?

A7 Apart from the Red Mason Bee, *Osmia rufa*, you can expect, depending on where you live, another two species of mason bee. These are *Osmia coerulescens*, the Blue Mason Bee and *O. leaiana* which has no common name. Both these species use finely chewed leaves rather than mud as a building material. *O. coerulescens* appears towards the end of the nesting period of *O. rufa* and is active from June to the end of July. It prefers slightly narrower tubes and does not use the nest kits as enthusiastically as *O. rufa*. This species is common and widespread in much of central and southern England and Wales and the females are good pollinators of clover.

Osmia leaiana is less widespread and common than *O. coerulescens* and, like that species, prefers slightly narrower nest tubes than *O. rufa*.

You are more likely to find that leaf-cutter bees, *Megachile* spp., will use the nester kits. As the name implies, these bees use pieces of cut leaf as a building material. They build thimble-sized cells entirely from leaves. There are three species that commonly use the nester kits. The smallest and earliest of these is the Rose Leaf-cutter Bee, *Megachile centuncularis*. It is active towards the end of *Osmia rufa*'s season and persists until the end of July. It is widespread and common in much of Britain, including Scotland. Despite its common name, *M. centuncularis* does not use rose leaves exclusively as a source of building supplies and, in fact, is rather catholic in its tastes. Females can often be seen collecting pollen from marigolds and other garden flowers of the daisy family. A larger and later species is *M. willughbiella*, and this is equally common and widespread. Its females are particularly fond of bell flowers (*Campanula* spp.), thistles (including ornamental forms), and they are excellent pollinators of peas and beans. Less common is *M. versicolor*, with a similar range of pollen sources.

Q8 *If, by providing nests for the Red Mason Bee, I build up populations to large levels, will I threaten other pollinators such as bumblebees and honeybees in my garden and in those of my neighbours?*

A8 No and for a number of reasons:

- *Osmia rufa* is active for no more than ten to twelve weeks in the year, whereas the social bumblebees and honeybee are active for eight to nine months.
- *O. rufa* is active in spring when bumblebee colonies have not yet built up to full size so that competitive interactions are minimal.
- while there is some overlap between bumblebees and *O. rufa* in terms of the flowers they visit, bumblebees have much longer tongues than the females of *O. rufa* and tend to visit flowers with deeper corolla tubes, so this is another way in which competition is avoided.
- bumblebees and honeybees need to collect and store large amounts of nectar in the form of honey whereas *O. rufa* stores only pollen, slightly moistened with a very little nectar. Thus, the social bees are largely nectar driven while the solitary bees, including *O. rufa*, are largely pollen driven. True, the social bees do gather pollen but, at any one time, not all the work force is engaged in this activity.
- many of the smaller solitary bees are active mainly towards the end of *O. rufa's* nesting period, with their peak of activity in mid- to late summer.

In short, wherever I have had *O. rufa* nests, I have never noted any deterioration in the abundance of other bees. In one garden of mine in Oxford, I recorded a total of fifty-four bee species while my present garden in Banbury boasts thirty-five species.

FIVE
The need to conserve our wild bees and what you can do

There are more than 250 species of wild bees native to Britain. Twenty-five per cent of them are on the *Red Data Book* list of endangered species. Five British bumblebee species (*Bombus* spp.) which, fifteen to twenty years ago, were widespread and common are now very rare and their ranges have contracted to a few small islands in a sea of intensive agriculture. Indeed, one of them, *Bombus subterraneus*, is now almost certainly extinct in Britain. And agriculture is one of the reasons for this decline.

This is not a dig at the poor beleaguered farmer. The farming community has responded magnificently to demands from government and populace alike that they should mass-produce cheap food. We need to take stock of our situation, however, and seek ways to redress the balance. And perhaps we should encourage farmers to see themselves as conservation and landscape managers, and make it worth their while financially to do so.

Modern intensive agriculture has produced a landscape which is no longer very bee-friendly. Since the end of World War II, we have lost 160,000 km of hedgerows. The logic behind their removal is that small fields are uneconomical when using modern, large farm machinery which needs plenty of room for manoeuvring. Moreover, there are real economies of scale in growing very large stands of crops, especially oil-seed rape and cereals such as wheat and barley.

The loss of much of our old hedgerows is a tragedy because these icons of the patchwork that makes up the typical English scene are a very important habitat: they mimic woodland edge which is a rich habitat for bees because of the diversity of the flowering plants they harbour with their rich sources of pollen and nectar for bees. They also house nest sites in the form of earth banks, old, hollow bramble and hogweed stems, and beetle borings in dead wood.

The loss of hedgerows and the marginal land associated with them has undoubtedly contributed to the decline in Britain's wild bees. Modern agriculture, with its emphasis on capital return, has no place for those corners of fields where old-style ploughs couldn't reach and where the farmer would stack old dead trees and logs.

Another cause of decline in our bees has been the loss of traditional hay meadows. With most cattle now being fed on silage, there has been little call for old-style hay-making in recent years. The mowing regime used to manage hay meadows maintained a high diversity of wild flowers which were a valuable forage resource for bees. Species such as devil's-bit scabious (*Knautia arvensis*), bird's-foot trefoil (*Lotus corniculatus*), knapweeds (*Centaurea* spp.), red clover (*Trifolium pratense*), yellow rattle (*Rhinathus minor*), red bartsia (*Odontites verna*), have all fallen in abundance since the decline of hay-making.

A recent study of those parts of Britain where the rare bumblebees mentioned above still survive showed that all had one thing in common: a lack of intensive agriculture and the persistence of hay-making or grassland management that maintained floral diversity, especially of plant species with longer corolla tubes, favoured by the longer-tongued bumblebees.

The general decline in the abundance and diversity of wild bees is a serious issue. Every third mouthful of human food is dependent either directly or indirectly on the unmanaged pollination services of bees. And it is not just for food that we depend on bees. Much of the visual impact of the landscapes we value for aesthetic reasons is the result of the network of mutually dependent relationships between bees and flowering plants.

The gradual erosion of our bee faunas is important for another reason: it is from within their ranks that we will have to recruit alternatives to the honeybee as a managed pollinator of crops, especially fruit. This is because apiculture has been in decline as a result of the devastation caused by the *Varroa* mite. Control measures for this parasite have made bee-keeping a more expensive and labour-intensive activity; in the last ten years, 40 to 45 per cent of the UK's bee-keepers have given up, and there has been a similar decline across Europe.

What you can do: planning a bee-friendly garden

As well as providing bees with nests, which is the main subject of this book, the simplest thing you can do to help our native bees is to grow flowers that they particularly like. A selection of traditional garden flowers is fine, including plants such as cranesbills and geraniums (*Geranium* spp.), wallflowers (*Cheiranthus* spp. and cultivars), stonecrops (*Sedum* spp.), deadnettles (*Lamium* spp.), sages (*Salvia* spp.), lavenders (*Lavandula* spp.), lamb's ears (*Stachys lanata*), custard-and-cream (*Limnanthes douglasii*), comfreys (*Symphytum* spp.), hound's tongue (*Cynoglossum officinale*), bugloss (*Anchusa* and *Echium* spp.), alkanet (*Alkanna* spp.), borage (*Borago officinalis*), mignonettes (*Reseda* spp.), and feverfew (*Tanacetum vulgare*).

All of the aromatic culinary herbs are valuable forage for bees and include thymes (*Thymus* spp.), oregano (*Origanum* spp.), and horehound (*Marrubium vulgare*). And most garden centres now sell seed mixtures of traditional meadow flowers.

In planning your bee-friendly garden, try to avoid double-flowered varieties. These monstrosities are a tribute to plant-breeders' ingenuity rather than wisdom: they are of no use to bees simply because the sexual parts of the flower, such as the pollen-producing anthers and the female stigma, have been replaced by whorls of extra petals and many have lost the ability to produce nectar.

SIX
Other solitary bees managed for pollination

Research in Italy, Holland, and Britain has shown that *Osmia rufa* is a highly efficient pollinator, especially of fruit crops. Yet we are only just beginning to exploit this useful insect. In this we are far behind the United States, Canada, and Japan where several solitary bees are managed very successfully as crop pollinators.

In North America and Canada, the best-known and most successful solitary bee exploited by farmers is the Alfalfa Leaf-cutter Bee, *Megachile rotundata*. Alfalfa (*Medicago sativa*) is an important forage crop for cattle. Like all members of the pea family, its flower has a spring-loaded release mechanism: when a bee probes the flower for nectar, its body weight on the lower 'keel' petals trips the mechanism and the anther-bearing stamens spring out and dust the underside of the bee with pollen.

Honeybees do not like this sudden tripping mechanism and avoid it by entering the side of the flower and therefore rarely effect pollination. Thus, when alfalfa was assuming importance as a forage crop in the United States and Canada, the hunt was on for an alternative to the honeybee as a managed pollinator.

The wild ancestor of cultivated alfalfa is not a native of North America: it originates in the Mediterranean region and the steppes and semi-deserts of Asia. By a stroke of pure good fortune, one of its native pollinators in the Old World, a tiny leaf-cutter bee, was accidentally introduced into North America and was discovered there some time in the 1930s. Exactly how this tiny bee crossed the Atlantic is unclear but it almost certainly got there because of its nesting habits: like *Osmia rufa, Megachile rotundata* is a typical cavity-nesting bee and nests in hollow plant stems and beetle borings in dead wood. Timber or plant material containing occupied nests was almost certainly imported into North America, perhaps as packing material, and thus human agency facilitated the migration of this bee to the New World.

In parts of Canada and the western United States, the rearing of this little bee for the pollination of alfalfa is now big business. And, if you drive through parts of California and Utah, you will see large trailers parked in alfalfa fields, each containing thousands of nests of *Megachile rotundata* made in wooden boards drilled for the purpose. The alfalfa growers hire the bee-trailers each year from firms that specialize in propagating the bee. When alfalfa flowering is over, the completed bee nests in their trailers are towed away, carefully overwintered and then hired out the following season.

There is another solitary bee which has been managed for alfalfa pollination, the Alkali Bee, *Nomia melanderi*. Unlike the Alfalfa Leaf-cutter Bee, this species is native to North America. It is a mining bee and is called the Alkali Bee because it likes to nest in dense aggregations in salt flats in the western United States. It is possible to construct earth banks around the margins of alfalfa fields with just the right soil texture and salt content to mimic its natural nest site, but it is difficult to maintain the right levels of soil moisture and it is much easier and cheaper to use the leaf-cutter bee, so the alkali bee is no longer used.

Mason bees have been introduced into the United States from Japan (*Osmia cornifrons*) and Spain (*O. cornuta*) for the pollination of orchard fruits. In Japan, *O. cornifrons* is managed commercially as a pollinator of apple crops, and *O. cornuta* has been used for almond pollination in California. The commercial exploitation of these imported bees is not yet developed and perhaps it never will be: a native species, the Blue Orchard Mason Bee, *O. lignaria*, has been shown to be a very efficient pollinator of several fruit crops, including almonds, apples, and cherries.

This species is widespread and common over much of North America and takes readily to the same sort of nest kits as suggested here for our own *O. rufa*. Though not yet managed on a large scale for commercial pollination, it has great potential and, in parts of the western United States, gardeners can purchase both nests and bees, and keeping this docile bee is a growing hobby.

Another native species, *O. ribifloris*, has been shown to be an effective pollinator of high bush blueberry in California, and at least three other native American species of *Osmia* have potential as managed pollinators.

It is clear that the wild bee faunas of our planet are an important natural resource, well worth studying and conserving.

SEVEN
Where to get your bee nester kits

Nester kits are available from the Oxford Bee Company Limited. and come in two sizes: 30-tube nest canisters and 100-tube nest canisters. Both come with a complete set of instructions. Replacement nest tubes are available separately.

For a price list and to order nest kits, contact:
The Oxford Bee Company Limited.
40 Arthur Street,
Loughborough,
Leicestershire
LE11 3AY
Tel: 01509 261654
Fax: 01509 261672
E-mail: oxbee2000@netscapeonline.co.uk

Or, you can visit our website at http://www.oxbeeco.co.uk, where there is a fund of information and a gallery of pictures of the Red Mason Bee, *Osmia rufa.*

From 2002 onwards, the Oxford Bee Company Limited. will be able to supply nest kits in which some of the tubes are occupied by overwintering bees. Such nests would be mailed in February, ready for the new spring season. Keep visiting the website to keep up to date with new developments and new products.

The Oxford Bee Company Limited. is a spinout company of Oxford University in conjunction with the University's Bee Systematics and Biology Unit and Isis Innovation Ltd, the University's technology transfer company.

Further reading

Buchmann, Stephen L. and Nabhan, Gary Paul, *The Forgotten Pollinators* (Shearwater Books, 1997), 320pp.
[An excellent account of just how we depend, for 80 per cent of our food, on the unmanaged pollination services of wild bees and other insects, and just how much the life-sustaining relationships between bees and plants are threatened by human degradation of habitats.]

Delaplane, Keith S. and Mayer, Daniel F., *Crop Pollination by Bees* (CABI Publishing, Wallingford, 2000), 344pp.
[A comprehensive overview of bees as managed crop pollinators in temperate regions.]

Griffin, Brian L., *The Orchard Mason Bee: The Life History, Biology, Propagation and Use of a North American Native Bee* (Knox Cellars Publishing Co., Washington State, 1999) 128pp.
[An easy-to-read account of *Osmia lignaria*, North America's cousin to the Red Mason Bee.]

O'Toole, Christopher, *Alien Empire: an Exploration of the Lives of Insects* (BBC Books, London, 1995), 224 pp.
[The book of the BBCtv series of the same name, this is a detailed account for the lay person of the ecological importance of insects for the rest of life on Earth.]

O'Toole, Christopher and Raw, Anthony, *Bees of the World* (Blandford Books, an imprint of Cassell, London, 1994), 192 pp.
[A comprehensive and highly illustrated account for the layman of the fascinating natural histories of bees from around the world.]

Field notes

	Date of first appearance of ♂♂	Date of first appearance of ♀♀	Date of first sealed nest	Date of last completed nest
Year 1				
Year 2				
Year 3				
Year 4				
Year 5				

Date	Flowers visited	
	♂♂	♀♀

Plate 1
A worker Honeybee, Apis mellifera, *at apple blossom with nearly full pollen baskets.*

Plate 2
A worker Garden Bumblebee, Bombus hortorum, *uses its long tongue to probe for nectar in the tubular flower of a primrose* (Primula vulgaris).

Plate 3
A female of the Dune Mason Bee, Osmia aurulenta, *seals her completed nest with a mastic of chewed leaves.*

Plate 4
A mating pair of the Red Mason Bee, Osmia rufa.

Plate 5
A female leaf-cutter bee, Megachile willughbiella, *cuts a piece of rose leaf to form part of a brood cell she is building.*

Plate 6

Emerging from her 'quarry', a female Osmia rufa *bears a glistening pellet of mud between her jaws, ready for use back at her nest.*

Plate 7

Carrying her ball of mud, a female Osmia rufa *returns to her nest in an old garden cane. Note one of the pair of stout horns beneath the antennae with which she presses her mud into the desired shape inside the nest. You can also see the dense scopa or fringe of specialized pollen-transporting hairs on the underside of her abdomen.*

Plate 8
Four completed cells of Osmia rufa, *each with a pearly white egg on its pollen store. Note the mud partitions between each cell.*

Plate 9
Feeding larvae of Osmia rufa.

Plate 10
A female Osmia rufa *covered with hundreds of mites,* Chaetodactylus osmiae. *Note the pairs of horns on the front of the head.*

Plate 11
A nest cell of Osmia rufa *(left) infested by larvae of the kleptoparasitic fly,* Cacoxenos indagator. *The fly larvae have starved the young bee larvae to death by eating all their food. Note the healthy silk cocoon (cell on right) containing a pupa of* Osmia rufa.

Plate 12
A pollen-dusted female of Osmia rufa *returns to her nest in an Oxford Bee Company Limited kit.*